Grades 6-8

Cloze

Comprehension in Context

George Moore

World Teachers Press

Order Number 2-5021
ISBN 1-885111-30-4

A B C D E F 96 97 98 99

Educational Resources

395 Main Street
Rowley, MA 01969

INTRODUCTION

Cloze is a well known teaching strategy for developing language skills. The author has used his extensive experience as a classroom teacher and principal to write this series of books which provides cloze exercises that are varied and interesting.

There are two main types of cloze exercises in this book – exercises where answer lists are given and those where the students provide their own words. In both cases, reading strategies such as context clues, syntactic and semantic skills and word recognition are practiced.

The factual stories enable the students to use their reading skills while learning interesting facts about a variety of topics. The imaginative stories will help to expand vocabulary and could be used as starting points for written expression.

Students should provide their own words in cloze review situations and not select words from a given list.

CONTENTS

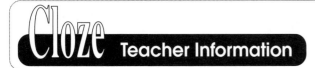

WHAT ARE CLOZE PROCEDURES?

Cloze is based on the gestalt idea of closure which states that we effect closure when we see enough parts of an entity, that is, the psychological impulse to complete a structural whole by providing a missing element.

The procedure provides information for teachers about how well readers detect deleted words, or parts of words, in a story by using context or pictorial clues.

Deleting content words (nouns, verbs, adjectives, adverbs) encourages the reader to search for meaning, whereas deleting structural word (conjunctions, pronouns, articles, prepositions), encourages the reader to use his/her knowledge of language to select words that are syntactically correct. The aim is to get responses which are both syntactically and semantically correct.

Example:

The man ate an ____axe____. The inserted word is syntactically correct, as the noun 'axe' following the indefinite 'an' is a correct placement in a sentence in the English language.

The man ate an ____apple____. This is syntactically and semantically correct as the sentence also has correct meaning.

The deletions may be random or at regular intervals, for example, every fifth, eighth, tenth word, and could include only certain parts of speech such as nouns and prepositions to suit a particular instructional lesson. This kind of lesson aims to develop the ability to search for meaning or the correct use of language, while at the same time reinforcing the students' knowledge of parts of speech.

TEACHING STRATEGIES

1. A number of writers and researchers have recommended cloze procedure as a suitable teaching method in reading. They believe students will gain insights into the process of using context, recognize the interrelationships of language, and consequently, improve comprehension skills, the most important aspect of reading.

2. The content of this book follows the advice of reading experts who recommend natural language and material which is interesting, for example, stories, reports, nonfiction, and poems.

3. Before cloze stories are given, you should use the chalkboard or an overhead projector to work orally through several simple, short stories with the class. This familiarizes the students with the method and class discussion shows that in some spaces several correct answers are possible.

4. Most reading authorities accept the use of synonyms in students' responses rather than the exact word. Some scoring systems also give partial credit for some responses, such as, incorrect spelling of common words.

5. Cloze procedures need to be an integral part of a reading program for it to be effective.

6. When using the review pages there should be no time limit. A review exercise can also be used to determine the level of other reading material a student could use.

7. A Teacher Information page precedes each Student Activity Sheet and includes a list of answers.

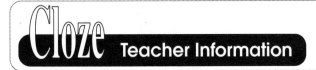
POINTS FROM RESEARCH ON CLOZE PROCEDURES

1. Cloze exercises are very effective in developing reading/listening skills with elementary/middle school students.

2. Selective deletions are effective as teaching tools and can be used to practice selected aspects of language such as nouns and verbs.

3. When introducing Cloze procedures teachers should precede written cloze exercises with oral cloze activities, for example, 'I rode to school on my _____.'

4. Except in test situations, cloze exercises can be used with partners or small groups – encouraging verbal interaction.

5. Prompts such as initial letters, pictures, and letter groups should be used in the initial stages when introducing the concept of Cloze Procedures to students.

REVIEWS (TESTS)

Interspersed through the book are review pages for testing purposes in which the students are not locked into using a list of words provided, but are able to use their own words as long as they fit into the story and retain the meaning of the text. This is a more creative approach and results in a fairly wide range of answers. Another advantage of this approach is that it takes into account the varying vocabularies of students with differing abilities in the language area.

Recording page

A

Exercises using pictorial and context clues.

Names	Ex no. —	Ex no. —	Ex no. —	Ex no. —	Ex no. —	Ex no. —	Ex no. —	Ex no. —

B

Exercises using context clues only.

Ex no. —	Ex no. —	Ex no. —	Ex no. —	Ex no. —	Ex no. —	Ex no. —	Ex no. —	Ex no. —

Results under sections A and B above can be compared in order to find the strengths and weaknesses of individual students.

 **Teacher Information**

Objectives:

1. To develop reading skills using cloze in a poetry format.
2. To encourage the search for meaning using context clues, nouns, verbs, and adjectives.

Teaching Points:

1. Discuss the poem's rhyming patterns which vary in some stanzas but remain constant in lines two and four.
2. Stress only one word is to be used in each space.
3. Conduct a brief discussion to define nouns, adjectives and verbs which are omitted from the poem.
4. Encourage the students to check the correctness of their entries by reading through each verse confirming, where necessary, that they fit in with the poem's rhyming pattern.

Evaluation:

1. How well did the students use the context, clues and rhyming patterns in the poem?
2. How well did the students participate in the class discussions?
3. Did the class enjoy the poem and understand the ideas expressed in it? For example, the meaning of "make memories of each darkened hour."

Answers:

1. moon
2. dead
3. lamp
4. light
5. golden
6. fingers
7. darkened
8. earth
9. warming
10. shafts
11. bough
12. Birds
13. notes
14. herald
15. spectacular

Use the list of words below to complete the spaces in the poem.
Remember to consider the rhyming words at the end of lines as this may help.

No _____, no stars

at _____ of night,

our earthly _____,

sheds no friendly _____.

On a _____ horizon

dawn's _____ explore

and make memories of

each _____ hour.

The cool dark _____

is _____ now,

and _____ of light

caress each _____.

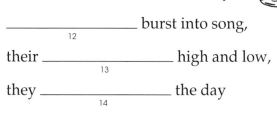

_____ burst into song,

their _____ high and low,

they _____ the day

a _____ show!

lamp	golden	moon	earth	Birds
bough	warming	herald	shafts	spectacular
dead	darkened	light	fingers	notes

Read the poem when completed to make sure it makes
sense. Use your dictionary to define new words.

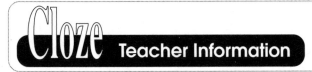

Objectives:

1. To develop reading skills using a cloze story on a subject familiar to the students.
2. To use cloze technique with both context and pictorial clues.
3. To encourage the search for meaning by omitting mainly nouns, adjectives, and verbs.

Teaching Points:

1. Conduct a class discussion on various aspects of sailing - safety, types of boats and America's Cup.
2. Conduct a brief discussion to define nouns, verbs, and adjectives which are omitted from the story.
3. Be sure students can read any unfamiliar words.
4. Remind students that pictorial clues will help with several answers.
5. Stress only one word is to be used in each space.
6. Encourage students to read each sentence when checking the correctness of the words inserted.

Evaluation:

1. How well did the students use the context and pictorial clues?
2. Did the students take an active part in the class discussion on sailing?

Answers:

1. tallest/highest
2. smallest
3. giant
4. yacht
5. only
6. on
7. sail
8. letters
9. clouds
10. shadows
11. towards/round
12. buoys
13. bird
14. fly
15. smoke
16. hills/mountains
17. reminds/tells
18. summer
19. anglers/fishermen
20. bobbers

Name: _____

Use clues in the picture to fill in the spaces in the story with **words of your own choice**.

The Esta building is the _____ on the city skyline, while the _____
1   2

skyscraper stands near the _____ crane. The largest _____ is the
3   4

_____ one with numbers _____ its _____ rather than
5   6   7

_____ like the other yachts.
8

The few _____ above cast no _____ on the water as the yachts race
9   10

_____ the first of the _____ outlining the course. A solitary
11   12

_____ watches the yachts, prepared to _____ away if danger threatens.
13   14

A plume of _____ rises from the _____ behind the city and
15   16

_____ us that _____ is here. The _____ ignore the racing
17   18   19

yachts and watch their _____ floating on the waves.
20

Objectives:

1. To develop reading skills using cloze with context clues in letter format.
2. To use the letter as a review to monitor progress with the students having to provide their own words for the spaces.
3. To reinforce the students knowledge of the layout of a letter.
4. To encourage the search for meaning by omitting nouns, adjectives, and verbs.

Teaching Points:

1. Discuss the layout of a letter - the address, the salutation (Dear.....) and closing (Yours sincerely...).
2. Discuss with the students what they think the person writing the letter is like. A successful, student, unmarried, a person catching up with an old friend.
3. Stress that only one word is to be used in each space.
4. Emphasize that each answer will be either a noun, an adjective or a verb and discuss the definitions of these parts of speech.
5. Encourage students to read each sentence when checking the correctness of their answers.

Evaluation:

1. How well did the students use the context clues?
2. Are the students more aware of the layout of a letter?
3. Did the students take an active part in the class discussions?

Answers:

1.	Aileen	11.	interesting
2.	long	12.	state/city
3.	wrote	13.	married
4.	happened	14.	lives
5.	brother	15.	older
6.	father	16.	interested
7.	new	17.	lawyer
8.	passed	18.	finish/end/go
9.	success	19.	hear
10.	hope	20.	birth

Name: _____

Use your own words to complete this letter.

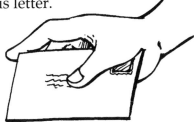

36 Vine Road
Dayton
Taylorville
October 24, 1996

Dear _____ ,
　　　　　1

It has been a _____ time since I last _____ to you and many things
　　　　　　　　　　2　　　　　　　　　　　　　　　　　3

have _____ during those years. My oldest _____ John is still at home
　　　　　4　　　　　　　　　　　　　　　　　　　　　5

with my _____ but my mother has remarried and now lives in Denton with her
　　　　　6

_____ husband.
　　7

I _____ my bar exam with great _____ and now _____
　　　8　　　　　　　　　　　　　　　　　　9　　　　　　　　　　　　　10

to find an _____ position with the Legal Aid Department in the _____
　　　　　　11　　　　　　　　　　　　　　　　　　　　　　　　　　　　　　12

offices.

I am not _____ yet but have a boyfriend who _____ in the same
　　　　　13　　　　　　　　　　　　　　　　　　14

suburb as I do. He is a lot _____ than I am but we are both _____ in
　　　　　　　　　　　　　15　　　　　　　　　　　　　　　　　　　16

the same things – movies and sport. He is also a qualified _____ and works in the
　　　　　　　　　　　　　　　　　　　　　　　　　　　17

Legal Aid Department.

Well, Aileen, I'll have to _____ now. Hope to _____ from you soon.
　　　　　　　　　　　18　　　　　　　　　　　　　19

Yours sincerely,

Mary

P.S. Happy to read about the _____ of your second daughter in St. Peter's
　　　　　　　　　　　　　　20
Hospital.

Objectives:

1. To develop reading skills using a cloze story with context clues.
2. To reinforce the students' knowledge of adverbs, especially adverbs of time.
3. To encourage the search for meaning by omitting adverbs.

Teaching Points:

1. Conduct a class discussion on adverbs - how they modify or add meaning to verbs.
2. Adverbs of time answer the question "when?"
   For example, John went later. Went when? Later. Ask for more examples from the students.
3. Discuss the situation of hospital visits to sick friends or relatives.
4. Remind students to read whole sentences when checking the correctness of their answers.
5. Stress that only one word is to be used in each space.

Evaluation:

1. How well did the students use the context clues?
2. Are the students more knowledgeable about adverbs and able to identify adverbs of time?
3. Did the students take an active part in class discussions?

Answers:

1.	daily	9.	then
2.	often	10.	hourly
3.	later	11.	never
4.	only	12.	before
5.	seldom	13.	afterwards
6.	recently	14.	always
7.	now	15.	sometimes
8.	soon		

Adverbs of time tell us when something is done
He played **now**, he came **recently**.
When did he play?   *Now*
When did he come?   *Recently*

Use the list of adverbs of time given below to complete the story.
Use a pencil in case you need to change answers.

David traveled to work in the city _____ and because of this he _____
1   2

heard free concerts in the city center. _____, however, he was told to go in
3

_____ on Tuesdays and _____ were concerts performed on that day.
4   5

He had said, only _____, that he would leave the firm if things changed, but
6

_____ he had a family which would _____ increase with the birth of
7   8

his latest child. David left the office at 5 p.m. and _____ he made sure he visited
9

his wife _____ in the hospital until 10 p.m. He looked forward to seeing his wife,
10

though he had _____ enjoyed visiting hospitals _____. He decided
11   12

_____ that he would _____ visit Jodie in the hospital and
13   14

_____ take their young children with him.
15

later	only	daily	recently	soon
never	always	then	hourly	sometimes
before	often	now	seldom	afterwards

Read the story through when completed to make sure it makes sense.

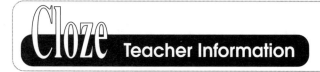
Objectives:

1. To develop reading skills using a nonfiction cloze story report about world famous explorers.
2. To encourage the search for meaning by omitting nouns, verbs, and adjectives.

Teaching Points:

1. Conduct a class discussion on why explorers explore unknown lands. For example, for trade, wealth, sense of adventure, or service to their country.
2. Encourage students to check the correctness of their answers by reading through each sentence to see if it makes complete sense.
3. Stress that only one word is to be used in each space.
4. Be sure the students can read any unfamiliar words in the story and the word list.

Evaluation:

1. How well did the students use the context clues.
2. Did the students take an active part in the class discussion?
3. Was the interest in the topic strong enough to lead to individual/group projects on famous explorers?

Answers:

1.	history	11.	voyage
2.	urge	12.	suffering
3.	unkown	13.	natives
4.	sailed	14.	courageous
5.	quest	15.	modern
6.	crossed	16.	walk
7.	frozen	17.	surface
8.	efforts	18.	millions
9.	treasures	19.	space
10.	life	20.	future

Name: _____

Use the words listed below to fill the spaces in the report.
When you have finished, you will know more about world explorers.
Use a pencil in case you need to change answers.

Exploration

Throughout _____ people have always felt a
            1

strong _____ to explore the vast _____ areas of the world.
          2   3

Christopher Columbus _____ west in an exciting _____ for new
                          4   5

lands, and a courageous Robert Falcon Scott _____ the barren, _____
                                                  6   7

wastes of Antarctica in his ill-fated _____ to reach the South Pole before
                                          8

Amundsen. Marco Polo brought back the _____ of Asia to Venice, and Magellan
                                            9

lost his _____ during the first _____ around the world.
            10   11

Unfortunately, many explorations have brought _____ to the conquered
                                                    12

_____ of the new lands discovered by these _____ explorers.
      13   14

In _____ times, Neil Armstrong's televised _____ on the moon's
        15   16

_____ was seen by _____ of people and promised even more
        17   18

exciting _____ exploration in _____ years.
              19   20

treasures	efforts	surface	future
sailed	history	quest	space
crossed	unknown	voyage	walk
urge	life	frozen	courageous
natives	suffering	modern	millions

Read the report when completed to make sure it makes sense.
Use your dictionary to define new words.

Objectives:

1. To develop reading skills by using context clues in a cloze story on an exciting subject.
2. To encourage the search for meaning by omitting mainly nouns, verb, and adjectives.

Teaching Points:

1. Discuss the characteristics of crocodiles.
   - a superbly designed hunter which hasn't changed over millions of years
   - fears of extinction have led to it being declared a protected species in different parts of the world
   - see if students can find out the difference between crocodiles and alligators
   - recent crocodile attacks in various parts of the world as reported in press
2. Be sure the students can read any unfamiliar words in the story and the word list.
3. Encourage the students to read each sentence when checking the correctness of their answers.
4. Stress that only one word is to be used in each space.

Evaluation:

1. How well did the students take part in the class discussion on the crocodile?
2. How well did the students use the context?

Answers:

1. fierce
2. silently
3. depths
4. antelope
5. water hole
6. refreshing
7. speed
8. snout
9. gleaming
10. spindly
11. terrified
12. vain
13. grip
14. dragged
15. muddy
16. shot
17. monster
18. stone
19. cocked
20. disappear

Name: _____

Use the words in the list to complete the spaces in the story.
Use a pencil in case you need to change your answers.

The Encounter

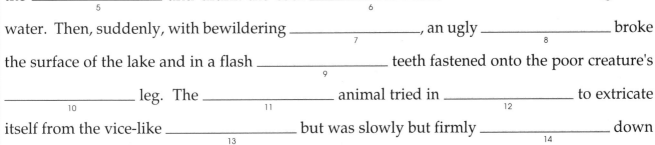

The _____ crocodile slid _____ into the
                    1   2

deep, dark _____ of the lake. A timid young
               3

_____ edged nervously down the sloping bank of
         4

the _____ and drank the cool _____
            5   6

water. Then, suddenly, with bewildering _____, an ugly _____ broke
                                                  7   8

the surface of the lake and in a flash _____ teeth fastened onto the poor creature's
                                               9

_____ leg. The _____ animal tried in _____ to extricate
        10   11   12

itself from the vice-like _____ but was slowly but firmly _____ down
                                  13   14

the lake's _____ bank.
                15

Then a loud _____ rang out and the huge
                     16

_____ sank like a _____ to
        17   18

the bottom of the lake. The smiling hunter

_____ his rifle again but it wasn't
        19

necessary and he watched the grateful antelope

_____ into the surrounding jungle.
        20

silently	shot	antelope	disappear
water hole	fierce	cocked	muddy
spindly	depths	refreshing	monster
vain	dragged	gleaming	grip
speed	snout	terrified	stone

Read the story when completed to make sure it makes
sense. Use your dictionary to define new words.

Objectives:

1. To develop reading skills by using context clues in a story on a familiar subject.
2. To omit pronouns and encourage the students to use syntactically correct words in their answers.
3. To reinforce their knowledge of pronouns.

Teaching Points:

1. Discuss the experiences of students who have bikes - the safety values of helmets, the usefulness of bikes for shorter distances, and bicycle thefts.
2. Discuss the use of pronouns to prevent the repetitive use of nouns.
3. Ask students to give examples of pronouns.
4. Point out that substituting pronouns can often be more difficult than substituting content words such as nouns and verbs.
5. Stress that a **different** pronoun should be used in each space.
6. Encourage the students to read each sentence to check the correctness of their answers.

Evaluation:

1. How well did the students use the context clues?
2. Are the students more knowledgeable about pronouns?
3. How did the students' results compare with those where content words rather than structural words were omitted?

Answers:

1. she
2. it
3. Her
4. his
5. they
6. them
7. We
8. I
9. He
10. me
11. us
12. One/You
13. our
14. mine
15. its

 **Pronouns**

Name: _____

Pronouns are words which we use in place of nouns to avoid repetition of nouns.

For example: *Overusing nouns:* John's mother gave John the book John's mother borrowed from John.

 Using pronouns: **His** mother gave John the book **she** borrowed from **him**.

Use a different pronoun in each space below.

Sandra had bought a new bike and _____ rode _____ each day.
                                              1   2

_____ husband Rob also rode _____ bike, but _____
        3   4   5

seldom rode _____ together. _____, (David and _____),
                    6   7   8

would sometimes see the two out together. _____ often waved but Sandra usually
                                                    9

ignored David and _____, though neither of _____ really cared.
                          10   11

_____ would have to be silly to do so and anyway, _____ lives were
        12   13

too interesting for such worries, _____ especially, with all _____
                                          14   15

exciting adventures from day to day.

Read the story when completed to make sure it makes sense.

Objectives:

1. To develop reading skills using context clues in a story of interest to the students.
2. To encourage the search for meaning by omitting adjectives.
3. To reinforce the students knowledge of adjectives.

Teaching Points:

1. Discuss any current western movies on TV or in the theaters.
2. Define adjectives and how they are used to describe nouns or pronouns.
   e.g. John is a **strong** boy.
   He is **strong.**
3. Ask the student to make up sentences containing adjectives. A word must be in context before it can be defined as a particular part of speech.
   e.g. He lifted the **iron** sword (adjective).
   Mother used the **iron** on my shirt (noun).
4. Be sure the students can read any unfamiliar words in the story and word list.
5. Remind the students that a dictionary can be used to check the meanings of more difficult words.
6. Encourage the students to read each sentence to check the correctness of their answers.

Evaluation:

1. How well did the students use the context clues?
2. Are the students able to recognize adjectives and the work they do in a sentence?
3. How well did the students participate in the class discussion?

Answers:

1. disastrous
2. hostile
3. local
4. urgent
5. triumphant
6. defeated
7. severe
8. successful
9. daily
10. empty
11. cordial
12. powerful
13. large
14. pleasant
15. different
16. booming
17. dilapidated
18. honest
19. native
20. northern

Adjectives are words which describe nouns - he is a **strong** boy, or pronouns - It (the box) is **heavy**).

The words to be used from the list below are all adjectives.
Use a pencil in case you need to change your answers.

When the _____ news about the attack by
1
_____ Indians reached the _____
2   3
newspaper office, several _____ discussions had
4
already taken place between the _____ war chiefs
5
and the _____ military officers.   The
6
_____ casualties suffered by the proud generals
7
meant the talks were not _____ at first.   Soon,
8
however, the _____ meetings held in an
9
_____ barn at noon began to succeed, thanks to the
10
_____ relations between the two leaders.
11

Chief Dark Eagle was a tall _____ man with a war bonnet
12
of _____ eagle feathers and a quiet, _____
13   14
manner at the peace talks. General Sheridan was totally
_____. His _____ voice dominated the
15   16
meetings in the old _____ barn, but he was an
17
_____ man who believed in the rights of all
18
_____ tribes in the _____ states.
19   20

triumphant	severe	disastrous	different	hostile
empty	powerful	pleasant	urgent	successful
local	daily	native	cordial	defeated
dilapidated	large	booming	honest	northern

Read the story through when completed to make sure it makes
sense. Use your dictionary to find unknown words.

 **Teacher Information**

Objectives:

1. To develop reading skills using context clues in a story of interest for the students.
2. To encourage the search for meaning by omitting verbs.
3. To reinforce the students knowledge of verbs.

Teaching Points:

1. Define verbs and explain that the missing verb could be one word or more than one word when the auxiliary part of the verb is present, for example, He was **going**, will be **going**. The auxiliary often denotes tense.
2. Ask the students to give examples of verbs with several parts.
   They **had gone**, we **have been** singing.
3. Discuss with the students what might be the thoughts of the people who have been shipwrecked. Has land been sighted? Will there be hostile savages? Will they have enough food if the land is deserted?
4. Encourage the students to read each sentence to check the correctness of their answers.

Evaluation:

1. How well did the students use the context clues in the story?
2. Can the students recognize the different parts of verbs?
3. Did the students take an active part in the class discussion?

Answers:

1. cleared
2. rowed
3. thundered/crashed/broke
4. gathered/appeared/formed
5. promised/threatened
6. sank/set
7. waved/brandished
8. waited/motioned
9. sobbed/sat
10. crouched
11. rescued/saved/salvaged
12. jumped
13. pointed
14. shaded/shielded
15. prayed
16. answered
17. watched
18. attacked
19. drove/forced
20. bordered/fringed

Name: _____

Verbs are mainly action words which tell us what someone or something has done, is doing, or will do. For example: the boy **jumped** the fence – **is jumping** the fence – **will jump** the fence.

Use your own verbs to fill the spaces in the story.
Use a pencil in case you need to change answers.

The skies _____ again after the storm and we slowly _____

towards the shore as waves _____ over the reef. More dark clouds

_____ over the mountains and _____ further heavy rain before the

red sun _____ below the horizon.

On the beach, angry natives _____ spears above their heads and

_____ for us to land. Tears running down their cheeks, the two women in the

boat _____ quietly and both _____ down behind the few supplies

Ray had _____ from the liner which now slowly disappeared beneath the waves

behind us. Suddenly, Cheryl _____ to her feet and _____ towards

the beach. We _____ our eyes from the sun and _____ that help was

near. Our prayers were _____! As we _____, a party of soldiers

from the ship _____ the natives and _____ them back into the jungle

which _____ the white, sandy beach.

Read the story through when completed to make sure it makes sense.

Objectives:

1. To develop reading skills using context clues in a story using only abstract nouns as answers.
2. To encourage the search for meaning by omitting only abstract nouns.
3. To reinforce the students' knowledge of abstract nouns.

Teaching Points:

1. Define abstract nouns and ask the students to give examples.
2. Encourage the students to scan the story to select the easier insertions from the list of nouns. This reduces the list of nouns and should make it easier to select the more difficult answers.
3. Discuss the suffering found in current trouble spots throughout the world to familiarize the students with the abstract concepts of cowardice, misery, and shame used in the story.
4. Encourage the students to read each sentence to check the correctness of their answers.
5. Be sure the students can read any unfamiliar words in the story.

Evaluation:

1. How well did the students use the context clues?
2. Can the students recognize abstract nouns and define them?
3. Did the students take an active part in class discussion?

Answers:

1. thought
2. idea
3. peace
4. hate
5. amazement
6. worry
7. fear
8. opinions
9. happiness
10. misery
11. confidence
12. shame
13. cowardice
14. memories
15. courage

 **Abstract Nouns** Name: _____

Abstract nouns are names of things which you cannot touch physically. For example, you can't grab hold of an idea in your hand and let people touch it; you can't take a piece of happiness and give it to your friend. Abstract nouns are often feelings such as love or fear.

All answers in the list below are abstract nouns. *Use a pencil in case you need to change answers.*

The _____ that only his _____ could bring _____ to a
country which had been torn apart by _____ surprised him. To his utter
_____ the only real _____ that concerned him was the gnawing
_____ that his outspoken _____ would not be accepted by his close
friends. However, he still believed the _____ his suggestion would bring could end
the _____ the citizens endured and a new _____ should sweep the land.
Any past _____ over the well–publicized _____ of frightened soldiers
in battle was to be forgotten and the more pleasing _____ of tales of outstanding
_____ would be passed on to future generations.

worry	shame	opinions
confidence	thought	memories
cowardice	happiness	hate
fear	peace	amazement
idea	misery	courage

Read the story when completed to make sure it makes
sense. Use your dictionary to define new words.

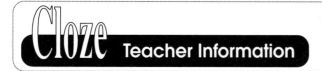
Objectives:

1. To develop reading skills using a cloze report on a familiar and interesting subject.
2. To encourage the search for meaning by omitting mainly nouns and verbs.
3. To give a general outline of the development of cars as a means of transport.

Teaching Points:

1. Discuss with the students the important part automobiles play in our life today.
2. Debate briefly the proposition: "Human beings and the environment would be better off without the car". Some points to consider:- ease of traveling, expense, pollution.
3. Be sure that the students can read any unfamiliar words in the story and the word list.
4. Encourage the students to read the sentence when checking the correctness of their answers.
5. Stress that only one word is to be used in each space.

Evaluation:

1. How well did the students use the context clues?
2. Are the students more familiar with the development of the car?
3. Are the students aware of both the advantages and disadvantages of the car?
4. Did the students take an active part in the class discussion?

Answers:

1.	engineers	11.	upright
2.	Benz	12.	streamlined
3.	inventing	13.	alloys
4.	automobiles	14.	airplanes
5.	compared	15.	strong
6.	Britain	16.	modern
7.	flag	17.	factories
8.	lamp	18.	craftsmen
9.	front	19.	produce
10.	pedestrians	20.	numbers

Name: _____

Use the list words below to fill the spaces in the passage. *Use a pencil in case you need to change answers.* You will learn some interesting information about cars.

Two German _____ named Daimler and
1

_____ are given the credit for _____ the
2   3

gasoline–driven engine first used in early _____. These
4

vehicles traveled very slowly when _____ with speeds
5

achieved today.

In those early days in _____ a person carrying a red _____ by day or
6   7

a red _____ at night had to walk in _____ of cars to warn
8   9

_____. Early models were _____ in design and not as
10   11

_____ as today's cars with their modern styles.
12

During World War II, many lightweight _____ were developed to make
13

_____ and these very _____ metals were later used in
14   15

_____ vehicles.
16

Today, our cars are mainly assembled in _____
17

and not built by individual _____ as they once
18

were. Henry Ford was the first man to _____ cars
19

in large _____ in his American factories.
20

produce	strong	flag	pedestrians	compared
inventing	Britain	upright	alloys	front
engineers	lamp	streamlined	airplanes	modern
factories	numbers	automobiles	craftsmen	Benz

Read the story through when completed to make sure it makes
sense. Use your dictionary to define new words.

Objectives:

1. To develop reading skills using cloze in a poetry format.
2. To encourage the search for meaning by omitting mainly nouns, adjectives and verbs.
3. To stimulate the students with an interesting subject.

Teaching Points:

1. Discuss the subject of U.F.O.'s (Unidentified Flying Objects) and the possibility of life on other planets.
2. Discuss the poem's rhyming patterns as an aid to finding the right word.
3. Be sure the students can read any unfamiliar words in the story and the list.
4. Stress that only one word is to be used in each space.
5. Encourage the students to check the correctness of their answers by reading each verse to be sure it makes sense and that the final word in the line follows the rhyming pattern.

Evaluation:

1. How well did the students use the context clues and rhyming patterns in the poem?
2. How well did the students take part in the class discussion?
3. Did the class enjoy the poem and the ideas expressed in it? For example, "an opportunity passed, wisdom gone astray".

Answers:

1.	Aliens	11.	formed
2.	land	12.	sought
3.	glowing	13.	love
4.	light	14.	earthlings
5.	clawed	15.	alone
6.	hand	16.	strangers
7.	friends	17.	naught
8.	night	18.	opportunity
9.	silent	19.	alliance
10.	above	20.	vanished

Name: _____

ALIENS!

Place the words from the list below into the spaces in the poem. Remember to use the rhyming patterns to help you.

_____ came from another _____,
     1   2

eyes _____ like moons in shadowy _____,
         3   4

_____ fingers on each scaly _____,
     5   6

they came to seek _____, they came by _____.
                7   8

A _____ descent from dark realms _____,
    9   10

spaceships _____ from metals unknown,
         11

they _____ friendship, progress and _____
     12   13

or do _____ prefer to exist _____?
      14   15

Our fear of _____ brought all to _____,
         16   17

an _____ passed, wisdom gone astray,
     18

they found no _____ eagerly sought,
         19

they _____ – perhaps to try another day.
     20

friends	earthlings	night	vanished	sought
silent	opportunity	above	light	Aliens
naught	strangers	love	hand	formed
land	alliance	alone	glowing	clawed

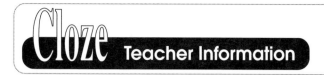
Objectives:

1. To develop reading skills using cloze in a poetry format.
2. To encourage the search for meaning by omitting adjectives.
3. Stimulate the students with a familiar subject.

Teaching Points:

1. Conduct a discussion about activities associated with the beach such as surfing, building sand forms, snorkeling, and collecting shells.
2. Conduct a brief discussion on adjectives as describing words which usually appear directly before a noun.
3. Stress that only one word is to be used in each space.
4. Encourage the students to check the correctness of their answers by reading through each verse to be sure it makes sense.

Evaluation:

1. How well did the students use the context clues in the poem?
2. How well did the students participate in the class discussion?
3. Were the students able to pair the adjectives with the appropriate nouns?

Answers:

1. distant
2. crashing
3. shore
4. rest
5. white
6. deserted
7. cool
8. blow
9. jagged
10. lengthening
11. sun
12. glowing
13. young
14. games
15. morning

Select the missing words from the list and put them into the spaces.
Use a pencil in case you make changes. Remember to consider rhyming words at the end of lines as this may help you select the right word.

At the Beach

On _____ reefs
₁

the breakers roam,

become _____ waves
₂

all rushing home,

they slide on the _____
₃

in breaking foam,

to _____ a while,
₄

to chase no more.

The long _____ beach
₅

is _____ now
₆

as a _____ north wind
₇

begins to _____,
₈

the _____ rocks on the broad headland
₉

cast _____ shadows
₁₀

across the sand.

As the _____ goes down
₁₁

in a _____ red
₁₂

the _____ beach-goers
₁₃

prepare for bed,

their day has gone,

the _____ are done,
₁₄

they now look forward

to the _____ sun!
₁₅

morning	glowing	crashing
games	distant	cool
shore	lengthening	white
deserted	rest	jagged
blow	young	sun

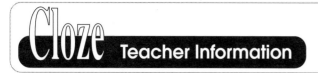

Objectives:

1. To develop reading skills using a cloze story on a familiar subject.
2. To encourage the search for meaning by omitting nouns, verbs, and adjectives.
3. To stimulate interest with a familiar subject.

Teaching Points:

1. Discuss the students' experiences regarding trains.
2. Discuss the vocabulary associated with trains, such as express, sleepers, stations, and the differences between the train in the picture and modern trains.
3. Be sure the students can read any unfamiliar words in the story and the word list.
4. Stress that only one word is to be used in each space.
5. Encourage the students to check the correctness of their answers by reading each sentence to see if it makes sense.

Evaluation:

1. How well did the students use the context clues?
2. How well did the students participate in the class discussion?
3. Are the students now familiar with the terms associated with the topic?

Answers:

1. train	11. slowly
2. station	12. staff
3. excited	13. uniforms
4. belongings	14. travelers
5. children	15. crowded
6. trash	16. empty
7. seats	17. waiting
8. silvery	18. hired
9. terminate	19. climbed
10. moments	20. task

 **The Trip**

Name: _____

When you have placed the words from the list into the spaces, read it again to make sure it makes sense. Check any unknown words in your dictionary and use a pencil at first in case you have to make changes.

The Trip

hired	task	crowded	climbed	uniforms
slowly	station	belongings	children	seats
trash	staff	excited	train	silvery
terminate	moments.	empty	travelers	waiting

As the _____ neared the _____ all the _____ passengers
          1   2   3
gathered their _____ together. Mothers fussed over their young
                    4
_____ and wrapped up any _____ left on the railroad car
      5   6
_____. The wheels sped over the _____ tracks and soon the long,
      7   8
monotonous journey would _____ after several hours of night travel.
                              9

A few _____ later the engine _____ rolled along the platform. The
          10   11
railroad _____ in their smart blue _____ helped to clear the crowd of
            12   13
_____ who _____ the platform and soon the station was
      14   15
_____ once more. Then the _____ team of workers
      16   17
_____ to clean the train _____ aboard and began their tiresome
      18   19
_____.
      20

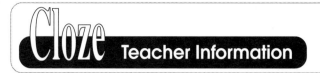 **Teacher Information**

Objectives:

1. To develop reading skills by using a cloze story with an interesting subject.
2. To encourage the search for meaning by omitting the adverbs.
3. To reinforce the students' knowledge of adverbs.

Teaching Points:

1. Ask the students to tell about any experiences they have had ice-skating or roller-blading.
2. Discuss adverbs and how they add meaning to verbs with emphasis on adverbs of manner.
3. Ask the students to give examples of sentences containing adverbs of manner ending in 'ly'.
4. Be sure the students can read any unfamiliar words in the story and word list.
5. Stress that only one word is to be used in each space.
6. Encourage the students to check the correctness of their answers by reading each sentence to see if it makes sense.

Evaluation:

1. How well did the students use the context clues?
2. How well do students understand the function of adverbs in a sentence?
3. How well did the students participate in the class discussion?

Answers:

1. Gracefully
2. slowly
3. rapidly
4. noticeably
5. anxiously
6. loudly
7. brilliantly
8. grudgingly
9. generously
10. awkwardly
11. heavily
12. bitterly
13. gradually
14. carefully
15. sadly

Name: _____

When you have written the words from the list into the spaces, read it again to make sure it makes sense. Check any unknown words in your dictionary and use a pencil in case you make changes.

All your answers are *adverbs of manner*. Most adverbs of manner end in 'ly' and they tell how something is done. For example: He ran **quickly**. How did he run? **Quickly**.

_____ the ice-skaters glided around the rink,
         1

_____ at first but then more _____ as
         2   3

the beat of the music quickened _____. Their
                                          4

parents watched _____ and applauded
                        5

_____ movements which were performed
         6

_____ by the young couple. Their opponents,
         7

_____, but also _____, applauded the
         8   9

great performance.

Then, without warning, Maria fell _____ and as they both crashed
                                            10

_____ to the ice, her parents saw she was crying _____. She had
         11   12

realized her chance for a medal was _____ disappearing.
                                              13

As the medical assistants carried her _____ from the scene, her unhappy partner
                                              14

walked _____ from the rink.
          15

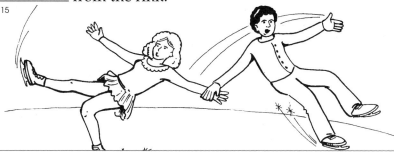

gradually	grudgingly	Gracefully	sadly	brilliantly
noticeably	slowly	heavily	rapidly	carefully
bitterly	generously	anxiously	awkwardly	loudly

Objectives:

1. To develop reading skills by using a cloze story on an interesting subject.
2. To encourage the search for meaning by omitting nouns, adjectives, and verbs.
3. To give dictionary practice to find the meanings of some words in the story.

Teaching Points:

1. Briefly discuss the courage and requirements of explorers who have explored unknown territory, such as Marco Polo, the astronauts, Livingstone.
2. Remind the students that dictionaries can be used for some of the difficult words in the story and word list.
3. Be sure that the students can read any unfamiliar words in the story and word list provided.
4. Stress that only one word is to be used in each story.
5. Encourage the students to check the correctness of their answers by reading each sentence to see if it makes sense.

Evaluation:

1. How well did the students use the context clues?
2. Did the students use their dictionaries effectively?
3. How well did the students participate in the class discussion?

Answers:

1. fearless
2. burning
3. died
4. heat
5. supplies
6. attacks
7. natives
8. reduced
9. clashes
10. forced
11. jungle
12. bitten
13. insects
14. river
15. friendly
16. canoes
17. rapids
18. flimsy
19. chance
20. safety

Name: _____

After you have placed the words from the list into the spaces, read the story again to be sure it makes sense. Check any new words in your dictionary and use a pencil in case you have to make changes.

The party of _____ explorers had crossed the
1
_____ desert but at great cost. Several horses had
2
_____ in the intense _____ and so some
3   4
_____ had to be left behind. Frequent savage
5
_____ by hostile _____ had also
6   7
_____ their numbers and more _____ were
8   9
expected in the future.

They now _____ their way through dense _____ and were constantly
10   11
_____ by a strange variety of tropical _____. At last they reached the
12   13
_____ where a _____ tribe would provide _____. The
14   15   16
dangerous, swiftly-moving _____ ahead would test the _____ boats
17   18
but it was their only _____ to reach Magamba and _____.
19   20

friendly	river	heat	natives
bitten	rapids	supplies	clashes
safety	reduced	died	forced
attacks	burning	canoes	fearless
chance	jungle	insects	flimsy

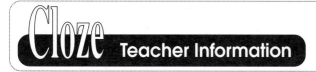 **Teacher Information**

Objectives:

1. To develop reading skills by using a cloze report on an interesting nonfictional subject.
2. To encourage the search for meaning by omitting nouns, adjectives, and verbs.
3. To familiarize the students with an outline of the history of flight.

Teaching Points:

1. Ask the students to relate any facts they know about airplanes and flight.
2. Be sure the students can read any unfamiliar words in the report and word list.
3. Stress that only one word is to be used in each space.
4. Encourage the students to check correctness of their answers by reading through each sentence to see if it makes sense.

Evaluation:

1. How well did the students use the context clues?
2. Are the students more aware of some stages in the development of aircraft?
3. How well did the students participate in the class discussion?

Answers:

1. yearned
2. ancient
3. believing
4. myth
5. attempts
6. escape
7. feathers
8. experimented
9. designed
10. propelled
11. successful
12. airplane
13. biplane
14. engine
15. fighter
16. millions
17. parts
18. unfortunate
19. conquest
20. destructive

Name: _____

Use the words in the list to fill in the spaces.

History of Flight

For thousands of years humans have _____ to fly. The
_____ Egyptians gave their god Khonsu wings,
_____ gods could do anything. A Greek _____ tells
about the _____ by Icarus and his father Daedalus to
_____ from the island of Crete using wings made from
_____.

The Montgolfier brothers in France first _____ with
balloons in the 1780s and the French also _____ the first
powered airship _____ by steam in the 1800s.

In 1903 in America, Orville Wright made the first
_____ powered _____ flight in a
_____ called the 'Wright Flyer'. In the 1940s the
first jet _____ designed by Englishman Harry
Whittle was used in a _____ plane.

Today, _____ of people travel in jets to all _____ of the world. It is
_____ the _____ of the air has been used in _____ ways.

parts	fighter	ancient	feathers	millions
escape	yearned	designed	airplane	destructive
attempts	myth	propelled	engine	successful
conquest	believing	biplane	unfortunate	experimented

Objectives:

1. To develop reading skills by using cloze in an fictitious newspaper report.
2. To encourage the search for meaning by omitting nouns, verbs, and adjectives.

Teaching Points:

1. Discuss with the students the characteristics of a popular newspaper report, such as, simple language, concentration of basic facts, reported in third person.
2. Read brief clippings on community issues.
3. Discuss how communities throughout the world have been affected by dams, for example, whole small communities being moved and rivers dammed to provide irrigation or hydroelectric power.
4. Be sure the students can read any unfamiliar words in the report and word list.
5. Stress that only one word is to be used in each space.
6. Encourage the students to check the correctness of their answers by reading each sentence to see if it makes sense.

Evaluation:

1. How well did the students use the context clues?
2. Are the students more aware of the style of newspaper reports?
3. How well did the students participate in the class discussions?

Answers:

1.	residents	11.	violence
2.	angry	12.	project
3.	government	13.	emphasizes
4.	flood	14.	people
5.	nature	15.	favorite
6.	beautiful	16.	many
7.	provide	17.	promised
8.	miles	18.	problem
9.	Protest	19.	headlines
10.	spokesperson	20.	channels

Use the words from the list to fill in the spaces in this newspaper report so that it makes sense.

NEWSPAPER REPORT

The _____ of the small country town of Alston are _____ ₂ !

They have just discovered that the State _____ ₃ has planned to _____ ₄ a local _____ ₅ area. A dam is to be built at the southern end of the _____ ₆ Edale Valley to _____ ₇ water to Stratton, a city forty _____ ₈ to the north.

_____ ₉ marches are planned and _____ ₁₀ Sandra Davey says the State will be to blame if _____ ₁₁ breaks out over the planned _____ ₁₂ .

She _____ ₁₃ that the valley has been used by _____ ₁₄ for thirty years and is the _____ ₁₅ picnic

area for _____ ₁₆ of the town's residents.

The local state representative has _____ ₁₇ to investigate the _____ ₁₈ , which has made _____ ₁₉ in this newspaper and featured in programs on two TV _____ ₂₀ .

Reporter: H. Baker

provide	nature	many	residents
Protest	flood	favorite	promised
channels	problem	angry	project
miles	headlines	people	violence
emphasizes	beautiful	government	
spokesperson			

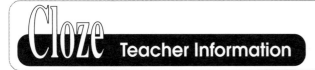 **Teacher Information**

Review

Objectives:

1. To develop reading skills using context clues in a letter format.
2. To use the text as a review to monitor progress with students having to provide their own words for the spaces in a text containing only context clues.
3. To encourage the search for meaning by omitting adjectives, nouns, and verbs.

Teaching Points:

1. Conduct a class discussion on exotic locations where students have spent vacations.
2. Show scenes of such locations in travel agent brochures.
3. Remind students of the correct letter format, that is salutation (Dear.....), writer's address, closing (Yours.....).
4. Stress only one word is to be used in each space.
5. Encourage the students to read each sentence when checking the correctness of their answers.

Evaluation:

1. How did the student's results compare with the other reviews where students had to provide their own words?
2. How did the results compare with stories in which picture clues were also provided?
3. How familiar are the students with the layout of a letter?
4. How well did the students participate in the class discussions?

Answers:

1. surprised
2. departure
3. fantastic/great
4. permit/allow/let
5. sports/activities
6. here
7. swimming/snorkeling
8. ocean/sea/water
9. fish
10. bothered
11. day/evening/night
12. acts/entertainment/shows
13. friendly/talented
14. guests
15. forward
16. wet/cool/winter
17. temperatures/weather
18. familiar
19. airport
20. next

Name: _____

Use **your own words** to fill in the spaces in the letter.

Room 17
Excelsior Hotel
Saraba

May 20, 1996

Dear Andy,

I suppose you are _____ to receive this letter so soon
  1

after our _____. Our hotel is just _____
  2   3

and I'm sorry your parents wouldn't _____ you to
  4

come with us.

All the _____ you enjoy are found
  5

_____. The _____ is great
  6   7

because the _____ is so clear, but the tropical
  8

_____ are not to be _____ in any
  9   10

way. Each _____ we watch first-class
  11

_____ put on by the _____ staff
  12   13

who want to be sure all _____ have a
  14

wonderful time.

I'm not looking _____ to returning to the _____ weather at
  15   16

home after the warm _____ here. Our return flight leaves on Saturday
  17

and we'll soon be in _____ surroundings once more. I hope you'll meet
  18

us at the _____ and that you'll be able to come with us on our
  19

_____ trip.
  20

Your friend,

Pete

Objectives:

1. To develop reading skills using context clues in a letter format.
2. To encourage the search for meaning by omitting mainly nouns, verbs and adjectives.
3. To reinforce the students' knowledge of the layout of a letter.

Teaching Points:

1. Discuss the advantages and disadvantages of a shopping trip with mother.
2. Discuss what happens to the old clothes the students have finished with - become hand-me-downs? Given to charity? Made into other articles?
3. Remind students of a letter format, i.e. salutation (Dear.....), closing (Yours .....), and writer's address.
4. Stress that only one word is to be used in each space.
5. Encourage the students to read whole sentences when checking the correctness of their answers.

Evaluation:

1. How well did the students use the context clues in the story?
2. How familiar are the students with the layout of a letter?
3. How well did the students participate in the class discussion?

Answers:

1. excited/thrilled
2. told/informed
3. clothes/dresses
4. styles/fashions
5. available/selling
6. prefer/appreciate
7. money
8. own
9. happen/occur
10. charity
11. need/want/require
12. wear
13. cut
14. strips/pieces
15. decorate/brighten
16. hanging
17. shoes
18. properly
19. repaired
20. pair

Fill in the spaces in Alison's letter with **your own words**.

3 Taylor Court
Ramsey

March 16, 1996

Dear Tricia,

I'm really _____ about going on a shopping trip this weekend. My

Mother _____ me last week that if I get rid of my old _____

she will buy me the latest _____ now that they are _____ in

the stores. I would _____ Mother giving me the _____ so I

can buy my _____ clothes, but that's not likely to _____.

I could donate my old dresses to a _____

to be given to people who _____

them as they have nothing nice to

_____. Or I could _____ up each

dress into small _____ and use the patterns to _____ plain

dresses _____ up in my wardrobe.

My _____ are so worn down I can't walk _____ so I'll have

to get them _____ as that is much cheaper than

buying a new _____.

Your friend,

Alison

Objectives:

1. To develop reading skills by using context clues in a story interesting to students.
2. To encourage the search for meaning by omitting nouns, verbs, adjectives, and adverbs.

Teaching Points:

1. Conduct a class discussion on haunted houses and ghosts. What are the students' opinions regarding their existence?
2. Stress that only one word is to be used in each space.
3. Be sure students can read any unfamiliar words in the story.
4. Encourage the students to read each sentence when checking the correctness of their answers.

Evaluation:

1. How well did the students use the context clues?
2. Did the students take an active part in the class discussion?

Answers:

1.	children/people	11.	explore/enter
2.	ever	12.	rooms
3.	house	13.	paintings
4.	haunted	14.	famous
5.	visitors/strangers	15.	sold
6.	heard	16.	money/funds
7.	avoid	17.	owners
8.	windows	18.	interested
9.	walls/bricks	19.	abroad/overseas
10.	dangerous/hazardous	20.	Uncle

Name: _____

Use your own words to fill in the spaces and make sense of the story.

None of the young _____ in
  1

the neighborhood _____ go
  2

near the old _____ which is
  3

said to be _____ by events in
  4

its past. Even _____ to the
  5

town have _____ the stories from local residents, so they _____
  6   7

going near the building.

Since the _____ are broken and
  8

the _____ are crumbling, it is
  9

considered to be _____ to
  10

_____ the many cobwebby
  11

_____ which still contain expensive _____. The artists are
  12   13

_____ so they are to be taken down and _____ to raise sufficient
  14   15

_____ to tear the building down.
  16

The original _____ of the property are not
  17

_____ in taking care of the building.
  18

They live _____ and only visit America
  19

to see an _____ who is their only living
  20

relative here.

 **Teacher Information**

Objectives:

1. To develop reading skills by using cloze story in a fictitious newspaper report.
2. To encourage the search for meaning by omitting mainly nouns and verbs.
3. To use a subject familiar to the students.

Teaching Points:

1. Discuss with the students the characteristics of a popular newspaper report such as simple language, concentration on basic facts, reported in third person.
2. Conduct a class discussion on volleyball - students who play, local teams, school teams.
3. Encourage the students to bring press clippings from local newspapers with reports about school teams.
4. Stress that only one word is to be used in each space.
5. Encourage the students to check the correctness of their work by reading through each sentence to see if it makes sense.
6. After completion of the exercise, discuss the skills/rules in volleyball and participate in a class game.

Evaluation:

1. How well did the students use the context clues?
2. Are the students more aware of the style of a newspaper report?
3. How well did the students participate in the class discussions?

Answers:

1.	students/children	11.	time/hours
2.	High	12.	deteriorated/suffered
3.	training/practicing	13.	pleased
4.	practice/improve	14.	volunteered/offered
5.	skills	15.	hold
6.	play-offs	16.	before/after
7.	important	17.	hope/want
8.	tall	18.	playing
9.	sport/game	19.	lose
10.	well	20.	affect/spoil

Name: _____

Use your own words to complete the report so that it makes sense.

_____

Newspaper Report

The _____ from 9th grade at
1
Lincoln _____ have been
2
_____ for weeks to
3
_____ their basic volleyball
4
_____. They are in the finals
5
of the local schools' _____ and
6
their skills levels are most _____.
7
Though being _____ is helpful in
8
this _____, even the shorter
9
players have performed _____.
10
In spite of all the _____ spent
11
practicing, the players' school work hasn't
_____, which has
12
_____their teachers. Parents
13

have _____ to help the team
14
and _____ the practice sessions
15
_____ school.
16

Though the players_____ to
17
win, the coach has stressed that
_____ well is just as important.
18
If they do _____, it shouldn't
19
_____ their enjoyment of the
20
sport.

Reporter: N. Rawlins

_____

Objectives:

1. To develop reading skills by using a cloze story.
2. To encourage the search for meaning by omitting nouns, verbs, and adjectives.
3. To reinforce the students' knowledge of reading information from a graph.
4. To develop the use of both context and pictorial clues.

Teaching Points:

1. Conduct a class discussion on safety measures at swimming pools and students' experiences of accidents.
2. Integration: Students could do their own graphics in a math lesson, on the various stages class members are at with their swimming skills, for example, nonswimmer, beginner, pool width.
3. Remind students that the picture will help with some answers.
4. Stress that only one word is to be used in each space.
5. Encourage the students to check the correctness of their work by reading each sentence to see if it makes sense.

Evaluation:

1. How well did the students use the context and pictorial clues?
2. Were the students able to read the graph correctly?
3. How well did the students participate in the class discussions?

Answers:

1.	lessons/sessions	11.	running
2.	pool	12.	wet/slippery
3.	week	13.	closed
4.	graph	14.	Mondays
5.	40	15.	poor/low
6.	Friday	16.	money
7.	35	17.	waiting
8.	eighth	18.	pool/water
9.	4 p.m.	19.	ladders
10.	diving	20.	times

Name: _____

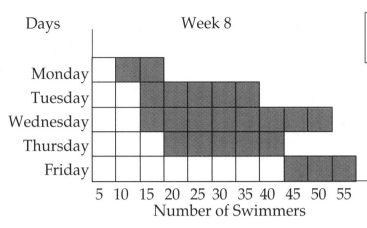

Days   Week 8

Days
Monday
Tuesday
Wednesday
Thursday
Friday

5 10 15 20 25 30 35 40 45 50 55
Number of Swimmers

SEAPORT POOL
Open 1p.m. - 4 p.m.

☐ Girls
▨ Boys

Using the information on the graph complete the story with your own words. No word is to be used twice and only one word is used in each space.

Swimming _____ are held at this _____ five days in each

_____ as indicated on the _____. There were _____
  3   4   5

girls and only 15 boys in the pool on _____, but _____ more boys
                 6   7

than girls attended lessons during the entire _____ week. There are no lessons
                     8

after _____ each day.
   9

At this pool there is no _____ and there is no _____ around because
              10   11

of the _____ tiles.
   12

The pool may be _____ in the future
            13

on _____ because attendance is so
   14

_____. On that day the complex
  15

does not take in enough _____ to
              16

cover the costs of keeping the pool open.

Three swimmers are patiently _____
                17

to climb out of the _____ as they are
           18

instructed to use the _____ at all
           19

_____.
 20

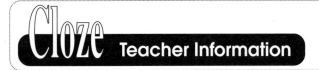
Objectives:

1. To develop reading skills using context and pictorial clues.
2. To use the text as a review to monitor progress when students have to provide their own words and to monitor how well the students use both context and pictorial clues.
3. To encourage the search for meaning by omitting nouns and adjectives.
4. To reinforce their graph and map reading skills.

Teaching Points:

1. Remind students that the graph and the map are to be used for some answers.
2. Be sure the students can read any unfamiliar words in the cloze story.
3. Remind the students that it is necessary to read the information paragraph to complete some of the answers.
4. Stress that only one word is to be used in each space.
5. Encourage the students to read each sentence when checking the correctness of their answers.

Evaluation:

1. How well did the students use both context and pictorial clues?
2. Were their graph and map reading skills of an acceptable standard?

Answers:

1.	Tacosa	11.	northern
2.	250	12.	rice
3.	interior	13.	dates/fruit
4.	desert	14.	July
5.	Ports/towns/cities	15.	40
6.	coast	16.	summer
7.	rivers	17.	southern/southerly
8.	January	18.	Beta
9.	February	19.	population
10.	winter	20.	mountains

Cloze Review

Name: _____

Saveria is a narrow country along the west coast of a continent. A mountain range affects its climate throughout the year. Because of the reliable rainfall, the coastal region produces all the food the country needs, especially huge quantities of rice, the most popular crop. The arid interior produces very little, apart from small shipments of dates to Tacosa.

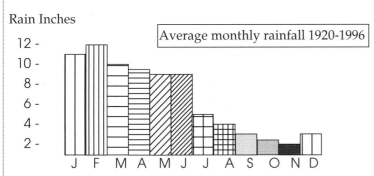

Rain Inches

Average monthly rainfall 1920-1996

Use the graph and map to complete the story.
Use a different word in each space.

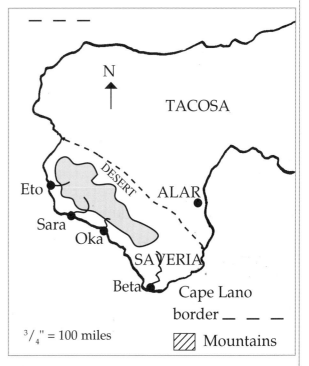

$3/4$" = 100 miles
▨ Mountains

Saveria's border with _____ is approximately _____ miles long. Most of the

country's _____ is arid _____ so the main _____ have been

built along the west _____ at the mouths of Saveria's main _____.

Most rain falls in _____ and _____. These

are the coldest _____ months as Saveria lies in the

_____ hemisphere.

The nation's staple diet is based on _____ and some _____ from the

interior areas are exported.

Beginning with the month of _____, a sudden decrease in rainfall by _____

inches indicates the start of the long, hot _____.

The most _____ city of _____ near Cape Lano has a _____

of only 35,000. Its average annual rainfall is not heavy as it is not influenced by the

_____.

About the Author

George Moore, has taught and lived in Perth, Western Australia, New South Wales (State), and the United Kingdom. George has been a practicing classroom teacher for over 30 years, with experience in primary and secondary areas. He has held promotional positions in England and Australia.